Illustrated by Graham Philpot

W
FRANKLIN WATTS

First published in 2009 by
Franklin Watts
338 Euston Road
London
NW1 3BH

Franklin Watts Australia
Level 17/207 Kent Street
Sydney
NSW 2000

Text © Anne Adeney 2009
Illustrations © Graham Philpot 2009

The right of Anne Adeney to be identified as the author
and Graham Philpot as illustrator of this Work has been asserted
in accordance with the Copyright, Designs and Patents Act, 1988.

A CIP catalogue record for this book is available
from the British Library.

ISBN 978 0 7496 8587 4 (hbk)
ISBN 978 0 7496 8591 1 (pbk)

Series Editor: Melanie Palmer
Series Advisor: Dr Barrie Wade
Series Designer: Peter Scoulding

Printed in China

Franklin Watts is a division of
Hachette Children's Books,
an Hachette UK company
www.hachettelivre.co.uk

Long ago, Jason's wicked uncle,
Pelias, stole Jason's kingdom.
He sent Jason to an island far away.

Now Jason wanted it back.

He went to the royal palace.

"Give me my kingdom, Uncle!"

he demanded.

"First, prove you deserve it. Bring me the Golden Fleece," replied Pelias, grinning. "You'll have to ask old King Phineus where it is."

Jason built a special ship for the quest, called the "Argo".

He called his crew of fifty mighty heroes the "Argonauts".

They sailed to the island where old King Phineus lived. Harpies, horrible birds with human heads, were attacking the King.

Jason's crew shot their arrows at
the Harpies and drove them away.

King Phineus was so grateful he told Jason where to find the Golden Fleece: "King Aites has it on the island of Colchis.

But beware of the Crashing Rocks," Phineus added. Jason smiled. He wasn't afraid of rocks!

But the rocks were huge!

They crashed together and

crushed everything between them.

Jason watched and had an idea.
When the rocks opened he sent
out a dove.

The rocks crashed ... but the dove
was through!

"GO!" Jason cried. The crew
rowed as fast as they could.
Then the rocks crashed again ...

... but the boat was through!

Jason sailed safely on to Colchis. "I've come to take the Golden Fleece," he told King Aites.

"First, tame my bulls, plough my field and sow these special seeds. Then I will give you the Fleece," said King Aites.

But the seeds were really dragon's teeth. Instead of plants, angry warriors sprang from the ground.

The warriors were made of bones. They didn't die, no matter how many times Jason used his sword.

So Jason threw a rock at one warrior.
"Who hit me?" yelled the warrior,
hitting another.

A fight began and soon all the warriors were dead and gone.

Jason went back to see King Aites.
"I'll never give you the Fleece!"
roared the King, angrily.

But the King's daughter, Medea,
had fallen in love with Jason.
"I'll take you to the Fleece," she said.

She led Jason to a dragon's lair.
By the dragon was a tree and
something gold and shiny.

The dragon breathed a ring of fire.
But Medea knew magic. She
charmed the dragon to sleep.

Jason leapt across the fire
and grabbed the Golden Fleece.
The Argonauts all cheered.

Medea joined Jason's ship and they sailed back to find Pelias.

Pelias was shocked to see Jason
return. He ran away in fear,
leaving Jason as the new King.

Puzzle 1

Put these pictures in the correct order.

Which event do you think is most important?

Now try writing the story in your own words!

30

Puzzle 2

Choose the correct speech bubbles for each character. Can you think of any others? Turn over to find the answers.

Answers

Puzzle 1

The correct order is

1e, 2a, 3f, 4b, 5c, 6d

Puzzle 2

Jason: 4, 6

Pelias: 1, 5

Medea: 2, 3

Look out for more Hopscotch Myths:

Icarus, the Boy Who Flew
ISBN 978 0 7496 7992 7*
ISBN 978 0 7496 8000 8

Perseus and the Snake Monster
ISBN 978 0 7496 7993 4*
ISBN 978 0 7496 8001 5

Odysseus and the Wooden Horse
ISBN 978 0 7496 7994 1*
ISBN 978 0 7496 8002 2

Persephone and the Pomegranate Seeds
ISBN 978 0 7496 7995 8*
ISBN 978 0 7496 8003 9

Romulus and Remus
ISBN 978 0 7496 7996 5*
ISBN 978 0 7496 8004 6

Thor's Hammer
ISBN 978 0 7496 7997 2*
ISBN 978 0 7496 8005 3

Gelert the Brave
ISBN 978 0 7496 7999 6*
ISBN 978 0 7496 8007 7

No Dinner for Anansi
ISBN 978 0 7496 8006 0

King Midas's Golden Touch
ISBN 978 0 7496 8585 0*
ISBN 978 0 7496 8589 8

Theseus and the Minotaur
ISBN 978 0 7496 8586 7*
ISBN 978 0 7496 8590 4

Jason's Quest for the Golden Fleece
ISBN 978 0 7496 8587 4*
ISBN 978 0 7496 8591 1

Heracles and the Terrible Tasks
ISBN 978 0 7496 8588 1*
ISBN 978 0 7496 8592 8

For more Hopscotch books go to: www.franklinwatts.co.uk

* hardback